Structured Tasks for English Practice

M000034884

conjunctions- compound and complex sentences

Written by
SUSAN D. LOPEZ, M.A.
LEONARD G. LANE, M.S.

Edited by
ELAINE COSTELLO, Ph.D.

Illustrated by
JAN WATKINS

KENDALL GREEN PUBLICATIONS
Gallaudet College Press
Washington, D.C.

Kendall Green Publications
An imprint of Gallaudet College Press, Washington, DC 20002
©1978 by Gallaudet College. All rights reserved

Published 1978. Third Printing, 1985
Printed in the United States of America
ISBN 0-930323-03-3
ISBN 0-930323-10-6 (Set)

Gallaudet College is an equal opportunity employer/educational
institution. Programs and services offered by Gallaudet College
receive substantial financial support from the U.S. Department
of Education.

FOREWORD

STRUCTURED TASKS FOR ENGLISH PRACTICE (STEP) is a series of programmed workbooks designed to assist deaf adults and young people in writing better English. The books in the series include: *Articles*; *Verbs: Past, Present, and Future*; *Nouns*; *Pronouns*; *Conjunctions*; *Adjectives and Linking Verbs*; *Adverb Clauses*; *Prepositional Phrases*; *Infinitives and Gerunds*; and *Writing Sentences*. The workbooks are intended to be used in conjunction with classroom lectures or for independent study. The self-instructional format provides opportunities for frequent student response, immediate feedback, and self-pacing.

The STEP Series is based on research which analyzed the errors made most frequently in the writing samples of deaf adults enrolled in the Gallaudet College Adult Basic Education classes during the fall of 1974. Revisions have been made which reflect the feedback from students and teachers using the developmental version of this workbook.

ACKNOWLEDGEMENTS

The authors wish to express appreciation to all of the people who helped in the various phases of the design and production of this workbook. These include:

- Thomas A. Mayes for his cooperation and enthusiastic support,

- Linda Donnels for her ideas and feedback,

- Mary Beth Ethridge for her many hours of work preparing the materials for publication, and

- The teachers and students in the Gallaudet College Adult Basic Education classes for their contributions in providing research data for this workbook's development and modifications.

TO THE TEACHER

This workbook is designed to be self-instructional. However, it is recommended that the student be encouraged to ask the meaning of unknown vocabulary and to ask for help when making excessive mistakes or not understanding what is expected.

A diagnostic test is available for use with the workbooks for two purposes: 1) to determine which concepts in which workbooks are needed, and 2) to determine, upon completion of the workbooks, if student learning took place.

Before the student begins to work in the workbook, the teacher should demonstrate how to read the directions, complete the exercise, and check the work by looking in the Answer Book after each page. The student should correct all mistakes.

For maximum effectiveness, the teacher may design additional activities to introduce, review, or expand the concepts presented in the workbook.

OBJECTIVES

RECOGNIZING CONJUNCTIONS - The student will circle all conjunctions and underline the words or groups of words which the conjunctions join in a given story.

USING CONJUNCTIONS - The student will write one sentence about each of two pictures using correct conjunctions in the sentences.

WRITING COMPOUND SENTENCES - The student will write at least five compound sentences about a picture.

WRITING COMPLEX SENTENCES - The student will write at least five complex sentences about a picture.

WRITING SENTENCES WITH CONJUNCTIONS - The student will write at least six compound and complex sentences about a picture.

TO THE STUDENT

★ Read and follow the directions on each page.
★ Look at the answers in the Answer Book.
★ Check your work and correct your mistakes.

CONTENTS

RECOGNIZING CONJUNCTIONS

Mrs. Goldstein **and** Mrs. Kelly

George **but** not James

Tabby **or** Sam

1

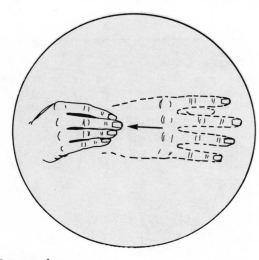

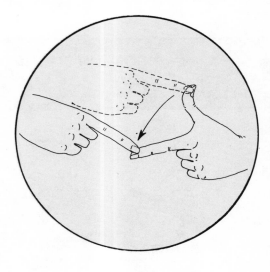

Example:

_____ *and* _____

1. _____

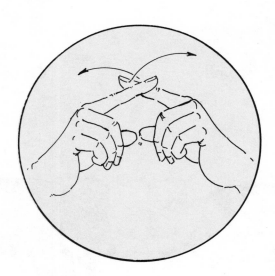

2. _____

2

1. in the afternoon

2. cats but not dogs

3. Mr. and Mrs. Lin

4. at the bus stop

5. peanuts and popcorn

6. on the train

7. tired but hungry

8. Christmas or Hanukkah

DIRECTIONS: **WRITE** YES **NEXT TO EACH SENTENCE THAT HAS A CONJUNCTION.**
DRAW A LINE UNDER THE CONJUNCTION.
WRITE NO **NEXT TO EACH SENTENCE THAT DOES NOT HAVE A CONJUNCTION.**

Example: _yes_   *My aunt <u>and</u> uncle left for Europe.*

      _no_   *My dog loves to bury bones in the yard.*

_____ 1. Virginia was one of the Thirteen Original Colonies.

_____ 2. Will you wear your uniform or regular clothes?

_____ 3. The longest day of the year is in June.

_____ 4. North and South Korea went to war in 1948.

_____ 5. We are friends but not neighbors.

1. Cottage cheese, lettuce, and sliced pears make a good salad.

2. I like ice skating but not roller skating.

3. Do you want ham, cheese, or tuna fish for lunch?

4. Ms. Stanford will go to Hawaii or California for her vacation.

5. My husband likes to shop for groceries but not for clothes.

6. The third and fourth grades will go to the zoo tomorrow.

7. Jessica wants to be an engineer or a lawyer.

8. Turn right at the corner of 16th Street and Pennsylvania Avenue.

9. Most fish swim downstream but not upstream.

10. Mr. and Mrs. Rickey will go to Florida on vacation.

11. Is morning, afternoon, or evening your favorite time of day?

12. We will re-cover the couch but not the chair.

4

CONJUNCTIONS JOIN WORDS OR GROUPS OF WORDS IN SENTENCES.

Laura and Maria are twins.

The conjunction **and** joined the names of two girls in this sentence.

DIRECTIONS: DRAW A CIRCLE AROUND THE CONJUNCTION IN EACH SENTENCE. DRAW A LINE UNDER THE WORDS OR GROUPS OF WORDS WHICH THE CONJUNCTION JOINS.

Example: *Please repair Ms. Sims' typewriter (but) not Ms. Tyson's.*

1. George felt happy but also tired.

2. Do you want a sports car or a family car?

3. Rita baked a cake, two pies, and some brownies.

4. Two or more people can sit at this table.

5. My sister can visit us Saturday but not Friday.

6. Ms. Winters and Mr. Benson went to Las Vegas and Reno.

7. We can watch the basketball game or the movie on television tonight.

8. Mr. Schultz likes tacos but not chili.

DIRECTIONS: DRAW A CIRCLE AROUND EACH CONJUNCTION IN THE STORY. DRAW A LINE UNDER THE WORDS OR GROUPS OF WORDS WHICH THE CONJUNCTION JOINS.

Example: You should never eat house plants (or) wild plants.

Poisonous Plants

Many plants, seeds, and flowers are poisonous. Some plants in your home and garden are poisonous. Apples are a good example. The seeds of an apple are poisonous but not the apple itself. Peach seeds and apricot seeds are also poisonous.

You should not eat wild mushrooms or berries. They may be poisonous. Some animals may eat poisonous and nonpoisonous plants. Certain plants are all right for animals but not for people.

USING CONJUNCTIONS

Do you want ketchup **or** mustard?

Joe likes basketball **and** hockey.

Mr. Foxx enjoys growing mums **but** not daisies.

DIRECTIONS: WRITE **AND, BUT,** OR **OR** TO COMPLETE EACH OF THE SENTENCES.

Example: Marvin likes to see plays ___but___ not movies.

1. Mrs. Frank cooked roast beef, potatoes, _____ green beans.

2. The Kleins will go to the game _____ not to the party.

3. Tom _____ Jerry are a cat _____ mouse team in cartoons.

4. Do you want a camera _____ a toolkit for your birthday?

5. They will go to Japan _____ to Africa this summer.

6. Sally _____ Cathy like to swim _____ not dive.

7. My son doesn't like peas, carrots, _____ spinach.

8. Everyone will go to the party _____ not together.

9. April, June, September, _____ November have 30 days.

10. The bus stops at the corner _____ not in the middle of the block.

DIRECTIONS: WRITE AND, BUT, OR OR TO COMPLETE THE SENTENCES IN THESE STORIES.

Example: Mr. McClellan likes to cook _but_ not to clean up.

Mr. McClellan likes to bake. He likes to bake bread, cakes, _____ pies. He doesn't like to bake cookies _____ brownies. He likes to surprise his wife _____ children with a delicious pie _____ cake. Sometimes Mr. McClellan bakes whole-wheat bread _____ cornbread _____ not white bread.

Mrs. Santini owns a clothing store. She sells dresses, pants, _____ many other things. She sells clothes for women _____ not for men. You can buy hats, dresses, sweaters, _____ night gowns. You may pay with cash, write a check, _____ use a credit card. Mrs. Santini will gift-wrap anything for you _____ not deliver it.

9

DIRECTIONS: ADD ONE OR MORE WORDS AFTER THE CONJUNCTION TO COMPLETE EACH OF THESE SENTENCES.

Example: Ms. Pond can roller-skate but _not ice-skate_ .

1. Many people like peanut butter and _____ sandwiches.

2. Mr. Johns plays tennis but _____ .

3. I need an "A" or _____ to pass this course.

4. The bus stops at the library but _____ .

5. Mrs. Todd, Mrs. Harmon, and _____ painted the fence.

6. Your sister or _____ must sign the form.

7. Did Mr. Sadler buy the brown suit or _____?

8. Mrs. Davis studied Spanish but _____ in college.

9. We sat on the beach and _____ the sea gulls.

10. The Taylors will go to Florida but _____ .

11. Mr. Brinson and _____ fished for a week.

12. People eat bacon and _____ for breakfast, lunch, or

_____ .

DIRECTIONS: ADD A CONJUNCTION AND ONE OR MORE WORDS TO COMPLETE EACH OF THESE SENTENCES.

Example: Do you want an artificial Christmas tree <u>or a real tree</u> ?

1. New York, Chicago, _____ are important American cities.

2. Will you vote for Mr. Smith _____ in the next election?

3. My grandmother used to feed the cows _____ every morning.

4. Why do you like golf _____ ?

5. Everyday Billy runs _____ at the playground.

6. Mr. Willowby _____ go bowling on Tuesday nights.

7. Do you want to read a magazine _____ ?

8. My friend gave me a party _____ for my birthday.

9. I packed my clothes _____ .

10. Ms. O'Riley likes to play tennis _____ .

11. Mr. and Mrs. Rogers will ride the train _____ to Florida.

12. Sunshine _____ make trees _____ grow.

DIRECTIONS: WRITE ONE SENTENCE ABOUT EACH PICTURE.
USE A CONJUNCTION IN YOUR SENTENCE.

Example:

The cat is playing but not the dog.

1._____

_____

_____

_____

2._____

_____

_____

_____

WRITING COMPOUND SENTENCES

PUT YOUR THOUGHTS TOGETHER WITH CONJUNCTIONS.

A COMPOUND SENTENCE IS `TWO COMPLETE THOUGHTS` JOINED BY A `CONJUNCTION`.

Mr. Evans owns a hardware store. `but` He does not sell paint.

Join these two complete thoughts with the word "but." Then you have a compound sentence.

Mr. Evans owns a hardware store, but he does not sell paint.

DIRECTIONS: **WRITE `1` NEXT TO THE SENTENCES WITH ONE THOUGHT.**
WRITE `2` NEXT TO THE SENTENCES WITH TWO THOUGHTS.

Example: __1__ *Corn grows in Kansas and Nebraska.*

__2__ *The United States began as 13 Colonies, but it grew into a great nation.*

_____ 1. Will you wear your new dress, or will you wear your blue pantsuit?

_____ 2. Mr. Chou wrote a long letter to his brother in Miami.

_____ 3. My daughter is a good student, and she plans to go to college.

_____ 4. Mr. Thompson likes to sail and to fish.

_____ 5. "Gone With the Wind" is a famous movie, but I have never seen it.

_____ 6. I will go to visit my friend, or my friend will meet me at the club.

THE NAMES OF PEOPLE, PLACES, OR THINGS IN THE FIRST PART OF A COMPOUND SENTENCE SHOULD NOT BE REPEATED IN THE SECOND PART. USE HE, SHE, IT, OR THEY INSTEAD.

Dr. Markum is an astronomy professor,
                                                 he
and ~~Dr. Markum~~ teaches at the university.

DIRECTIONS: DRAW A LINE THROUGH THE NAME IN THE SECOND PART WHICH WAS USED IN THE FIRST PART OF EACH SENTENCE BELOW. WRITE HE, SHE, IT, OR THEY ABOVE THE NAME.

Example: Shelley is a key punch operator, and ~~Shelley~~ does volunteer
                                                                    she
work at the hospital on weekends.

1. The President went to England, and the President met the Queen.

2. Margaret likes basketball, but Margaret doesn't like football.

3. Mr. Duchman is a good boss, and Mr. Duchman is also handsome.

4. Mrs. Swanson bakes at least three pies, or Mrs. Swanson doesn't bake at all.

5. Canada is our neighbor, and Canada is a beautiful country.

6. Mr. and Mrs. Watts bought land, and Mr. and Mrs. Watts will build a cabin.

7. The swimmers saw the lifeguard waving, but the swimmers couldn't hear him.

8. The stop sign fell down, or the stop sign was knocked down.

DIRECTIONS: WRITE HE, SHE, IT, OR THEY IN THE BLANK IN EACH SENTENCE.

Example: Mrs. Bright bought some apples, and __*she*__ gave them to her students.

1. The man wore a grey suit, and _____ wore a red and grey tie.

2. The train will leave at 6:05, and _____ will arrive in New York at 10:00.

3. Mr. and Mrs. Stevens didn't go to class, but _____ studied their lesson.

4. Mr. Swanson will go to Miami, or _____ will go to New Orleans next week.

5. The girl made her bed, and _____ hung up her clothes this morning.

6. The clouds will go away, or _____ will bring rain.

7. The bird took a bath, and then _____ sat on the fence.

8. Ms. Watson washed her hair, but _____ couldn't roll it up.

9. The students saw the film, and _____ talked about it in class.

10. The boy saw the snake, but _____ didn't scream.

11. Elizabeth Taylor visited the college, and _____ answered questions.

12. My watch fell on the sidewalk, but _____ didn't break.

DIRECTIONS: THE CONJUNCTIONS IN THESE COMPOUND SENTENCES ARE CIRCLED.

DRAW A LINE UNDER EACH OF THE TWO COMPLETE THOUGHTS WHICH THE CONJUNCTION JOINS.

Example: The Vanns are going on vacation, (but) they must get their car ready first.

1. My boss bought a new picture for the office, (but) she hasn't hung it on the wall yet.

2. The Simpsons have three dogs, (but) they don't have any cats.

3. The Mackenzies have a farm, (and) they have seven horses.

4. Do you want the trunk in the basement, (or) do you want it in the attic?

5. My sister bought a house, (but) she doesn't have any furniture.

6. My husband applied for a job at the bank, (and) I applied for a job at the college.

7. Mr. Diego planted the vegetables, (and) Mrs. Diego planted the flowers.

8. Can you babysit tonight, (or) do you have other plans?

9. We will paint the kitchen, (and) then we will buy a new kitchen table.

10. The Post is a good newspaper, (or) do you prefer the Star?

11. Will the train stop in Alexandria, (or) will it go to Washington?

12. Virginia became a state in 1788, (but) West Virginia didn't become a state until after the Civil War.

DIRECTIONS: DRAW A CIRCLE AROUND THE CONJUNCTIONS IN THESE COMPOUND SENTENCES.
DRAW A LINE UNDER EACH OF THE TWO COMPLETE THOUGHTS.

Example: I have a pencil, (and) he has some paper.

1. Give me a raise, or I will quit!

2. Mr. and Mrs. Jones will fly to Europe, but they will return by ship.

3. Our children play at the playground, but they must be home before dark.

4. Ms. Harwood comes from Maine, and she loves lobster.

5. The Boswell's dog barks all night, and it keeps everyone awake.

6. Mrs. Mann is allergic to poison ivy, but she is not allergic to poison oak.

7. Would you like iced tea, or do you prefer a beer?

8. Go to the car, and wait for me.

9. Will you come to my house, or should I come to your house?

10. The airplane left on time, but it didn't arrive on time.

11. The Whites celebrated their anniversary yesterday, but I forgot to buy them a gift.

12. Does Jim like to go to the theatre, or does he prefer sports?

DIRECTIONS: JOIN EACH OF THESE TWO COMPLETE THOUGHTS WITH A CONJUNCTION TO MAKE A COMPOUND SENTENCE.

Example: *I will go to the beach tomorrow,* _but_ *my husband will not come until Sunday.*

1. The children played ball outside, _____ the adults played cards inside.

2. Mrs. Gravely wanted a blue coat, _____ she got a red one instead.

3. We can cook dinner here, _____ we can eat at the Pizza Parlor.

4. I wanted to arrive on time, _____ I was an hour late.

5. Does your husband mow the lawn, _____ does he pay Bobby to do it?

6. My friend went bike riding, _____ I went with him.

7. My daughter is a majorette, _____ my son is on the track team.

8. Mr. White tried to find his car keys, _____ he couldn't find them.

9. Clean up your room, _____ don't go to the basketball game tonight.

10. We saw "Shields and Yarnell" on TV, _____ it was a very good show.

11. He is wrong, _____ he won't admit it.

12. Don't tell my secret, _____ I won't tell you another one.

THE TWO COMPLETE THOUGHTS IN A COMPOUND SENTENCE MUST BE ABOUT THE SAME THING.

WRONG: Mrs. Smithers is a seamstress, and I have a headache.

RIGHT: Mrs. Smithers is a seamstress, and she makes beautiful clothes.

DIRECTIONS: PLACE A ✔ NEXT TO EACH CORRECT COMPOUND SENTENCE.

Example:

___✓___ *Mr. Banning went bowling, and Mr. Brodsky went with him.*

_____ *The maid dusted the furniture, and the dog buried his bone.*

_____ 1. Mr. Matthews took the Boy Scouts fishing, but his own son stayed home.

_____ 2. Herb found a dollar on the sidewalk, and Rita learned to use the calculator.

_____ 3. The children will go on a trip today, but their mother will stay at home.

_____ 4. The United States has a Congress, and Great Britian has a Parliament.

_____ 5. Do you like to visit your mother-in-law, or do you like to grow a mustache?

_____ 6. Africa is a large continent, and it is made up of many different countries.

Example: __2__ My sister left for vacation today, ...

__1__ Geraldine wants a 10-speed bike, ...

1. but she can't afford one.

2. and her family went with her.

COLUMN A

_____ Alaska is the largest state in the United States, ...

_____ The first day of spring is in March, ...

_____ The Petersons may drive to California, ...

_____ The police department does a good job, ...

_____ Would you like to go out tonight, ...

_____ A large office building has many clerical workers, ...

_____ Texas is a big and beautiful state, ...

_____ Ms. Stanski found a wallet in the store, ...

_____ The Marlowes will look for a new apartment, ...

COLUMN B

1. but there is still a lot of crime.

2. or do you prefer to stay at home?

3. but it doesn't have a lot of people.

4. and she left it at the "Lost and Found" desk.

5. or they will buy a new house.

6. and it also has many custodial workers.

7. and the first day of summer is in June.

8. but it gets very hot there in the summer.

9. or they may fly to Hawaii.

FOLLOW THESE STEPS TO WRITE A COMPOUND SENTENCE.

1 Write one complete thought. Put a comma after it. ⟹ The plumber came to repair the sink,

2 Select the correct conjunction. ⟹ and

3 Write another complete thought. Make sure your two complete thoughts are about the same thing! ⟹ the electrician came to repair the porch light.

DIRECTIONS: WRITE **1** NEXT TO SOMETHING YOU WOULD USE FOR STEP 1 IN WRITING A COMPOUND SENTENCE.
WRITE **2** NEXT TO SOMETHING YOU WOULD USE FOR STEP 2.
WRITE **3** NEXT TO SOMETHING YOU WOULD USE FOR STEP 3.

Example: __2__ but

__3__ the dog chased the cat.

__1__ Some stores were closed,

1. _____ the ice was too thin.

2. _____ Several people saw the smoke,

3. _____ and

4. _____ The parade began at noon,

5. _____ or

6. _____ will he pay the bill?

7. _____ Do you want coffee,

8. _____ but

22

Example: *It is getting late. I do not want to go home. (but)*

It is getting late, but I do not want to go home.

1. It is spring. The flowers are blooming. (and)

_____

_____

2. Mr. Darwin made a bookshelf for his wife. His wife wanted a sewing table. (but)

_____

_____

3. Some people like to live in the city. Some people like to live in the country. (and)

_____

_____

4. Will they have a picnic? Will they go to the amusement park? (or)

_____

_____

5. The children will stay with their grandmother for three weeks. My husband and I will stay home. (but)

_____

_____

6. Did the team win the tournament? Did they lose it? (or)

_____

_____

Column 1	Column 2	Column 3
My cat sleeps all day	and	her husband takes the bus.
Please hurry	or	will you send your son?
My mother owns a dairy farm	but	he prowls around at night.
Mrs. Williamson drives the car to work		she raises prize-winning cows.
Mr. Godfrey likes to cook		we will be late.
Will you go to the store		his wife likes to work on the cars.

Example:

My cat sleeps all day, but he prowls around at night.

1. _____

2. _____

3. _____

4. _____

5. _____

DIRECTIONS: **JOIN EACH GROUP OF SENTENCES WITH A** **CONJUNCTION** **TO MAKE A COMPOUND SENTENCE.**

Example: *I have a German shepherd. Bruce has a Saint Bernard.*

I have a German shepherd, and Bruce has a Saint Bernard.

1. That painting is very good. You need a little more blue.

   _____

   _____

2. It is raining. We will go on a picnic anyway.

   _____

   _____

3. The new furniture arrived today. We sold the old furniture.

   _____

   _____

4. Ivey has a lot of work to do. Barbara has more.

   _____

   _____

5. You better stop cheating. I won't play cards with you anymore.

   _____

   _____

6. The Kaufmans followed the officer's directions. They soon found the college.

   _____

   _____

DIRECTIONS: **WRITE THE STORY BELOW AGAIN USING** COMPOUND SENTENCES.

Example: *Our dog was gone three days. Then he came home.*   *Our dog*

was gone three days, and then he came home.

Our dog Bullet became sick. We had to take him to the vet.

_____

_____ We didn't want to. We had to. _____

_____ The doctor examined Bullet. He

said our dog needed some medicine. _____

_____

_____

The dog could have pills. He could have a shot. _____

_____

We chose the shot. The vet gave the dog one. _____

_____

_____

We went home. Bullet had to stay at the hospital. _____

_____

DIRECTIONS: ADD A `CONJUNCTION` AND `ANOTHER COMPLETE THOUGHT` TO EACH COMPLETE THOUGHT BELOW TO MAKE A COMPOUND SENTENCE.

Example: Mr. and Mrs. Collins will take a second honeymoon, *and they will go to Hawaii.*

1. My brother-in-law is an electrician, _____

_____

2. We often have summer thunderstorms, _____

_____

3. My cat and dog have flea collars, _____

_____

4. Earthquakes cause a lot of damage, _____

_____

5. Tomorrow I must pull the weeds from the garden, _____

_____

6. Ms. Darrow will be a witness at a court trial, _____

_____

7. January and February are the coldest months of the year, _____

_____

8. The Averys sold their big house, _____

_____

DIRECTIONS: ADD A COMPLETE THOUGHT AND A CONJUNCTION TO EACH COMPLETE THOUGHT BELOW TO MAKE A COMPOUND SENTENCE.

Example: _The mechanics voted to strike_ ,

but the drivers voted not to strike.

1. _____ ,

   _____ the men baked the cakes.

2. _____ ,

   _____ do you want to go to jail?

3. _____ ,

   _____ the man couldn't find his way home.

4. _____ ,

   _____ Mrs. Farmer didn't see it.

5. _____ ,

   _____ will he go fishing?

6. _____ ,

   _____ I don't like prunes.

7. _____ ,

   _____ then they went shopping.

8. _____ ,

   _____ the judge wouldn't accept his answer.

DIRECTIONS: WRITE ONE COMPOUND SENTENCE ABOUT EACH PICTURE.

Example:

They will buy a cat, or they will buy a dog.

1. _____

_____

_____

_____

2. _____

_____

Example: The parents want their children to win, or they will be disappointed.

WRITING COMPLEX SENTENCES

COMPLEX SENTENCES MAKE YOUR LANGUAGE MORE INTERESTING. USE CONJUNCTIONS SUCH AS **BECAUSE**, **SINCE**, **SO**, **IF**, **BEFORE**, AND **AFTER** IN COMPLEX SENTENCES.

Mrs. Thompson just got back from a vacation in Florida, **so** she has a lovely tan.

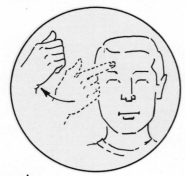

Example:

___*because*___

1. _____

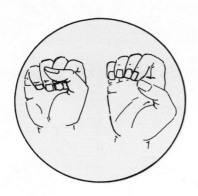

2. _____

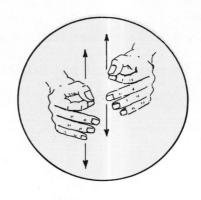

3. _____

4. _____

5. _____

A COMPLEX SENTENCE IS AN INCOMPLETE THOUGHT JOINED TO A COMPLETE THOUGHT. THE INCOMPLETE THOUGHT BEGINS WITH A CONJUNCTION.

Conjunctions often used
in complex sentences:

because	if
since	before
so	after

Here is a complex sentence:

She put on a sweater | because she was cold.

COMPLETE
THOUGHT

INCOMPLETE
THOUGHT

DIRECTIONS: **PUT A ✔ NEXT TO EACH COMPLETE THOUGHT BELOW.
PUT AN X NEXT TO EACH INCOMPLETE THOUGHT.**

Example: ___✓___ *my son is a skate board champion*

___X___ *if I go on a diet*

_____ 1. March is a windy month

_____ 2. after they were married

_____ 3. because the pond is very deep

_____ 4. we don't have much time

_____ 5. since I found a $5.00 bill

_____ 6. the cat scratched the dog on the nose

A **COMPLEX SENTENCE** IS AN INCOMPLETE THOUGHT JOINED TO A COMPLETE THOUGHT. THE INCOMPLETE THOUGHT BEGINS WITH A CONJUNCTION SUCH AS **BECAUSE,** **SINCE,** **SO,** **IF,** **BEFORE,** OR **AFTER.**

DIRECTIONS: WRITE **YES** NEXT TO EACH COMPLEX SENTENCE AND DRAW A LINE UNDER THE **CONJUNCTION.**
WRITE **NO** NEXT TO EACH SENTENCE WHICH IS NOT A COMPLEX SENTENCE.

Example: _no_ Katherine and Michael painted their porch.

yes Morris is in many TV commercials, <u>so</u> he is a very famous cat.

_____ 1. Franz went to visit relatives in Europe.

_____ 2. I had been sick before I was caught in the rain.

_____ 3. Please come by my house if you get a chance.

_____ 4. Ms. Nunnally received an invitation to the banquet.

_____ 5. Farmers must rise early since they have so much work to do.

_____ 6. Will you spend the night in Richmond?

_____ 7. Sesame Street is a popular children's TV show.

_____ 8. Dinner will be served at 6:30 after the guests arrive.

_____ 9. Many historical buildings are in good condition.

_____ 10. The government requires warnings on cigarettes because smoking isn't good for your health.

DIRECTIONS: DRAW ONE LINE UNDER THE COMPLETE THOUGHT IN THE COMPLEX SENTENCES BELOW.
DRAW A CIRCLE AROUND THE CONJUNCTION IN EACH SENTENCE.

Example: Mr. Olson didn't buy a new car (because) he couldn't afford it.

1. Paul was late for work because he overslept.

2. I will go with you if you want me to.

3. Mrs. Taylor will type that letter after she eats lunch.

4. His luck has changed since he came to Washington.

5. Your car may not start if you forget to turn the lights off.

6. Our company made a lot of money last year, so I got a raise.

7. Ms. Karas missed some of the movie because she was late.

8. Frances and Ken always eat dinner after they watch the news.

9. Sharon saved her money before she took a vacation.

10. A storm is coming, so we cannot go sailing.

11. Not many people want to live in Greenland since it is so cold.

12. Mr. Tomlin wanted to drink a cup of coffee before he shaved.

DIRECTIONS: **DRAW ONE LINE UNDER EACH COMPLETE THOUGHT IN THE SENTENCES IN THE STORY BELOW.**
DRAW TWO LINES UNDER EACH INCOMPLETE THOUGHT IN THE SENTENCES.

Example: <u>Many people like to go to California</u> <u><u>because there is so much to see and do</u></u>.

Traveling Across the U.S.A.

Traveling around the United States can be fun if you like to travel. You may want to go all the way to Alaska. Alaska is a very wealthy state because it has so much oil. However, you may not want to go that far. You should go to the Rocky Mountains if you are interested in wildlife. Arizona is a good place to visit because the Grand Canyon is there. Plan to spend a lot of time in Texas since that state is so big! Water skiers and sailors will love the Great Lakes. Don't forget about the East and West Coasts if you like pretty beaches.

THE COMPLETE THOUGHT AND THE INCOMPLETE THOUGHT MUST MAKE SENSE WHEN THEY ARE PUT TOGETHER IN A COMPLEX SENTENCE.

The sentence below does not make sense.

We will go skiing since your suit is brown.

COMPLETE THOUGHT

INCOMPLETE THOUGHT

We will go skiing since it is snowing.

The sentence above makes sense.

DIRECTIONS: PUT AN X NEXT TO EACH SENTENCE THAT DOES NOT MAKE SENSE.

Example: ____X____ *She will win the dance contest if it snows.*

_____ *We bought a van because it was on sale.*

_____ 1. George Washington had false teeth after your son broke my vase.

_____ 2. Mr. Gonzales will talk to the boss if he has to work late again tonight.

_____ 3. The bees were swarming around the picnic because they were afraid of fire.

_____ 4. My wife helped me prepare my income taxes, so I took her to dinner.

_____ 5. The Baltimore Orioles did not win the World Series since they did not play a very good game.

Example: __2__ I didn't have enough money to fix the car ...

1. if she has time.

__1__ She will help us move ...

2. so I charged it.

COMPLETE THOUGHTS

_____ Venus and Mars are the planets closest to the Earth ...

_____ Rinny is a very beautiful dog ...

_____ Many people like Farrah Fawcett-Majors ...

_____ We will get a trophy ...

_____ I must finish school ...

_____ They will move to Utah ...

_____ Dieters like watermelon and canteloupe ...

_____ William Shakespeare was a famous English writer ...

_____ A lot of people like to go shopping in January ...

_____ Mr. Koslo is president of the Lions Club ...

INCOMPLETE THOUGHTS

1. if you like German shepherds.

2. before I can get a good job.

3. since there are many after-Christmas sales.

4. so someday you might be able to fly there.

5. after they sell their house.

6. because she is so beautiful.

7. if our team wins this game.

8. because they do not have many calories.

9. since he wrote many great plays.

10. so he has a lot of responsibility.

DIRECTIONS: JOIN THE COMPLETE THOUGHT AND THE INCOMPLETE THOUGHT
WITH A CONJUNCTION TO MAKE A COMPLEX SENTENCE.

Example: *Many things have happened to her* ___*since*___ *she finished school.*

```
                      CONJUNCTIONS
         because        so        before
         since          if        after
```

1. Jerry couldn't run in the race _____ he had a broken leg.

2. Mrs. Gilmore will get a raise _____ she does good work.

3. Mark will play basketball this year _____ his grades improve.

4. They will not come to the barbeque _____ they don't like to eat meat.

5. My cat likes to go outside _____ it's not raining.

6. Nancy must mail the letter _____ the post office closes.

7. Fred drove his car to work _____ he could leave early.

8. Mrs. Jacobs was happy _____ she got a new job.

9. Margaret won't come to class _____ she has a visitor from out of town.

10. We want to do something special for the children _____ we are taking them to the Puppet Theatre.

DIRECTIONS: ADD AN INCOMPLETE THOUGHT TO EACH OF THE COMPLETE THOUGHTS BELOW TO MAKE A COMPLEX SENTENCE.

Example: *Our friends gave us a party,* so we stayed out late last night.

1. Mr. LeGrand won a model car race _____
_____

2. My nephew must learn better manners _____
_____

3. Most high school students study U.S. history _____
_____

4. The United States is a great country _____
_____

5. Mr. Mann will go to the dance with Ms. Cummings _____
_____

6. Your dog is very lazy _____
_____

7. Mrs. Schwartz has done a lot of traveling _____
_____

8. Our family was arguing about the TV _____
_____

DIRECTIONS: **ADD A** **COMPLETE THOUGHT** **TO EACH OF THE INCOMPLETE THOUGHTS BELOW TO MAKE A COMPLEX SENTENCE.**

Example: *Ms. Whittaker is afraid to stay home alone* since she saw the scary movie.

1. _____

_____ so I will pass the test.

2. _____

_____ because the jury found him "not guilty."

3. _____

_____ since they heard that the plane would be late.

4. _____

_____ because their coats were alike.

5. _____

_____ so their children could see Santa Claus.

6. _____

_____ since the chair was broken.

7. _____

_____ so the car would be warm.

8. _____

_____ because we were hungry for fish.

COMPLEX SENTENCE = COMPLETE THOUGHT + INCOMPLETE THOUGHT.
The incomplete thought begins with a conjunction.

COMPOUND SENTENCE = COMPLETE THOUGHT + COMPLETE THOUGHT.
A conjunction joins the two complete thoughts.

DIRECTIONS: PUT AN X NEXT TO EACH COMPLEX SENTENCE BELOW.
PUT A ✓ NEXT TO EACH COMPOUND SENTENCE BELOW.

Example: ___✓___ *Mr. Todd was invited to the party, but he can't go.*

___X___ *The woman was late to work because the bus broke down.*

_____ 1. The electricity was off, so Mr. Martin couldn't watch TV.

_____ 2. Mrs. Steele went to the dentist, and she was there 2 hours.

_____ 3. Some of the people wanted to ski, but the others wanted to sit by the fireplace.

_____ 4. Mrs. James took Carl to school after they went to the doctor.

_____ 5. The women sat on chairs, and the men sat on the floor.

_____ 6. The plane couldn't land because the fog was too thick.

_____ 7. Our football players can win the game if they try.

_____ 8. Will the class meet tonight, or has it been cancelled?

_____ 9. Mr. Barber will stop at the store before he goes home.

_____ 10. The sun was shining, but it was a very cold day.

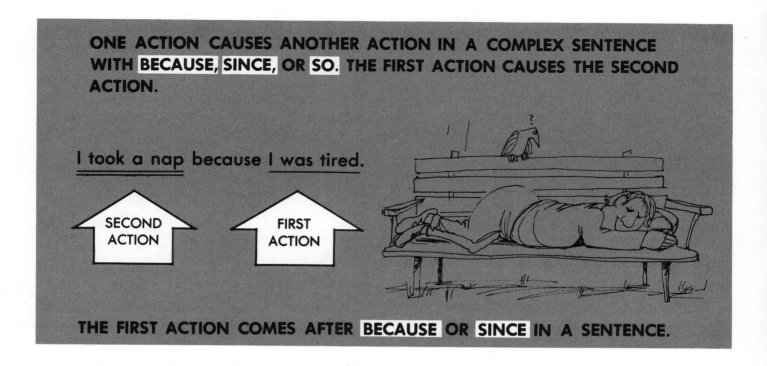

ONE ACTION CAUSES ANOTHER ACTION IN A COMPLEX SENTENCE WITH BECAUSE, SINCE, OR SO. THE FIRST ACTION CAUSES THE SECOND ACTION.

I took a nap because I was tired.

SECOND ACTION

FIRST ACTION

THE FIRST ACTION COMES AFTER BECAUSE OR SINCE IN A SENTENCE.

DIRECTIONS: **BECAUSE** AND **SINCE** ARE CIRCLED IN EACH OF THESE SENTENCES. DRAW A LINE UNDER THE **FIRST ACTION** IN EACH SENTENCE.

Example: Melvin doesn't want to go to the hospital (because) he is afraid to have an operation.

1. The Lions beat the Tigers (since) it was a better team.

2. The boy left camp early (because) he was homesick.

3. She doesn't want to drive downtown (since) the traffic is heavy.

4. I will help you with your work (since) I am not busy.

5. Ms. Hill doesn't want to learn bookkeeping (because) it is so difficult.

6. Mr. Lund can't go to the party (because) he has to work.

ONE ACTION CAUSES ANOTHER ACTION IN A COMPLEX SENTENCE WITH BECAUSE, SINCE, OR SO. THE FIRST ACTION CAUSES THE SECOND ACTION.

He was late, so he ran home.

FIRST ACTION SECOND ACTION

THE FIRST ACTION COMES BEFORE SO IN A SENTENCE.

DIRECTIONS: SO IS CIRCLED IN EACH OF THE SENTENCES BELOW. DRAW A LINE UNDER THE FIRST ACTION IN EACH SENTENCE.

Example: You have finished school, (so) *now it is time for you to earn your own living.*

1. We bought a swimming pool for the children (so) they can enjoy the hot summer days more.

2. Mr. French worked 5 hours overtime this week (so) his family could have a little extra money.

3. They will have their cat spayed (so) she will not have more kittens.

4. Phyllis didn't have enough money for a bookcase, (so) she made one with boards and bricks.

5. Our apartment doesn't allow pets, (so) we will have to move.

DIRECTIONS: DRAW A LINE UNDER THE FIRST ACTION IN EACH SENTENCE.

Example: *Don't pick the tomatoes* **since** *they aren't ripe yet.*

1. The cheap brand of gasoline clogged my carburetor, **so** I changed brands.

2. We could smell the fresh bread **because** the wind was blowing toward us.

3. Ms. Corning paid to have the machine fixed **since** she broke it.

4. The moving company will take good care of your furniture, **so** don't worry.

5. You cannot pick up your sewing machine yet **because** you haven't paid the bill.

6. The train is too slow, **so** we will take an airplane.

7. We should cook the meat a little bit longer **since** it is still rare.

8. I have to buy the children some new clothes **since** school starts next week.

9. Mr. Stanley belongs to a chess club, **so** he has people to play chess with.

10. Marty doesn't want to go to the dance **because** he doesn't dance very well.

11. They didn't eat in the park **since** it began to rain at noon.

12. The dog couldn't jump the fence, **so** it crawled under the gate.

1. We were tired of waiting, **so** we went to the play without them.

2. I will be home tonight **so** you can come to visit me.

3. Ted wants a new blow dryer for his birthday **because** his old one broke last week.

4. Mr. Matthews took a long vacation **because** he did not have a vacation last year.

5. The children did not have to go to school today **since** it snowed four inches last night.

6. The Stallone sisters returned to New York **so** they could visit their family and friends.

7. Brenda has a good idea **because** it will save our club some money.

8. My mother is babysitting **so** my husband and I can celebrate our anniversary.

9. Mr. Bradford didn't write me a letter **since** he didn't know my address.

10. We put the birds in the bathroom **so** we could clean out their cage.

11. Smoke alarms are important **because** they warn people of fires.

12. The baby hasn't cried **since** I fed her.

1. The library didn't open until 9:00, so we had to wait outside for 10 minutes.

2. The little boy cried because he was afraid.

3. We don't go to the movies much since we bought a giant screen color TV.

4. Belinda's car had a dent, so she took it to have it fixed.

5. The union leader will talk to management since we did not get our puy increase.

6. The shelf in the kitchen needs to be replaced, so I will need to buy a piece of wood.

7. The soldiers went on leave because the sergeant dismissed them.

8. In January we went to Vermont since it is so beautiful there in the wintertime.

9. The mountain climber climbed all day, so he was very tired that night.

10. The police detective arrested the wrong person because he did not gather enough information about the crime.

DIRECTIONS: WRITE YES NEXT TO EACH SENTENCE WHICH HAS THE CORRECT CONJUNCTION BECAUSE, SINCE, OR SO.
WRITE NO NEXT TO EACH SENTENCE WHICH DOES NOT HAVE THE CORRECT CONJUNCTION.
WRITE THE CORRECT CONJUNCTION ABOVE EACH INCORRECT ONE.

Example: ___*yes*___ My son's birthday is today, so I bought him a cake.

since
___*no*___ I went home ~~so~~ it started to rain.

_____ 1. It was a beautiful day so we had the party outside.

_____ 2. The Kinneys are moving next week because they will need our help.

_____ 3. It was their silver wedding anniversary, so we gave them a silver gravy boat.

_____ 4. Colorado is a beautiful state since we plan to go there on vacation.

_____ 5. We were hot and perspiring so we played tennis.

_____ 6. It was the 4th of July because Mr. Bright bought some fireworks.

_____ 7. Allan wants to buy his wife some flowers since he wants to make her happy.

_____ 8. The store was giving free tickets to the circus so we went shopping there.

_____ 9. She was late to work so she had to change a tire on her car.

_____ 10. Most people like to sleep on Saturday because they don't have to go to work.

DIRECTIONS: WRITE BECAUSE, SINCE, OR SO IN THE BLANKS IN THE SENTENCES.

Example: [I want to go to bed early _since_ I am tired.]

1. Mr. and Mrs. Chiang gave us two puppies _____ they had too many.

2. My sister and her husband will go to a party tonight _____ I will babysit for them.

3. Our church is planning a garage sale _____ we can earn money for a school.

4. The United States is a democracy _____ we have a "government by the people."

5. I like to go to the Astor Restaurant _____ it has good food.

6. Mrs. Clay will not have lunch today _____ she can lose some weight.

7. Ms. Gladstone wants to sit down _____ her legs hurt.

8. They plan to work hard Saturday morning _____ they can bowl Saturday afternoon.

9. Eat your vegetables _____ you will grow up to be strong and healthy.

10. I don't like to argue _____ it is a waste of time.

11. Mr. Taub has been feeling better _____ he had his surgery.

12. We decided to stay home _____ the streets were slippery.

49

1. I will not have to water the garden _____

_____

2. Mr. Lincoln cannot come to the meeting _____

_____

3. Don't wash the dishes _____

_____

4. Please come to my house _____

_____

5. The children want to have a picnic _____

_____

6. Thanksgiving is a nice time of the year _____

_____

7. The Governor visted the college _____

_____

8. Leon has a good job _____

_____

Example: We will leave for the airport exactly at 7:30, *so please be ready on time.*

1. We do not have any milk _____

_____

2. Mark knows all about taxes _____

_____

3. The Howes left us their house key _____

_____

4. The post office is on strike _____

_____

5. It will be a cold winter _____

_____

6. We bought a used car _____

_____

7. Our son had a fever _____

_____

8. The vaccum cleaner is broken _____

_____

IT IS EASY TO CHANGE A BECAUSE OR SINCE SENTENCE TO A SO SENTENCE. JUST MOVE THE FIRST ACTION TO THE BEGINNING OF THE SENTENCE. ADD SO. THEN ADD THE SECOND ACTION.

We ran for shelter because it started to rain.

first action

It started to rain, so we ran for shelter.

DIRECTIONS: CHANGE THESE BECAUSE AND SINCE SENTENCES TO MAKE THEM SO SENTENCES.

Example: Sandra rode her bike to work because her car needed repairs.

Her car needed repairs, so Sandra rode her bike to work.

1. Ms. Parker is on a diet since she is overweight.

_____

_____

2. I took my umbrella because it was raining.

_____

_____

3. We went to New Orleans since my father-in-law was ill.

_____

_____

4. Mr. Blankman wore his brown suit since his blue suit was dirty.

_____

_____

IT IS EASY TO CHANGE A SO SENTENCE TO A BECAUSE OR SINCE SENTENCE. JUST START THE SENTENCE WITH THE SECOND ACTION. ADD BECAUSE OR SINCE. THEN ADD THE FIRST ACTION.

I lost my car keys, so I had to take the bus.

second action

I had to take the bus because I lost my car keys.

DIRECTIONS: CHANGE THESE SO SENTENCES TO MAKE THEM BECAUSE OR SINCE SENTENCES.

Example: Someone robbed it last night, so the bank is not open today.

The bank is not open today because someone robbed it last night.

1. My sister loves horseback riding, so she bought a horse.

_____

_____

2. Mr. Roberts is a business expert, so the university asked him to give a lecture.

_____

_____

3. The ice was thin, so Mr. Barker couldn't ice skate.

_____

_____

4. The tailor needed more room, so he moved to a new shop.

_____

_____

PEOPLE HAVE REASONS **FOR DOING THINGS. YOU CAN FIND OUT THE REASON FOR SOMETHING BY ASKING** WHY.

Why are you so dirty?

I am dirty **because** I changed the oil in my car.

BECAUSE, SINCE, **OR** SO **ARE USED IN THE ANSWER OF A WHY QUESTION.**

DIRECTIONS: FINISH THE ANSWER TO EACH WHY **QUESTION BY ADDING** BECAUSE **AND THE FIRST ACTION.**

Example: Why will your daughter go to college?

My daughter will go to college *because she wants to be a lawyer.*

1. Why do you want a salad for lunch?

   I want a salad for lunch _____

2. Why will Mr. Sturgis work late tonight?

   Mr. Sturgis will work late tonight _____

3. Why can't Aunt Ruth come to visit us?

   Aunt Ruth can't come to visit us _____

4. Why did the Clarks go camping?

   The Clarks went camping _____

5. Why are her parents moving to Arizona?

   Her parents are moving to Arizona _____

54

SOMETIMES BECAUSE AND SINCE HAVE THE SAME MEANING.

Why is Mr. Uberman painting his house?

Mr. Uberman is painting his house **because** he plans to sell it.

Mr. Uberman is painting his house **since** he plans to sell it.

DIRECTIONS: FINISH THE ANSWER TO EACH WHY QUESTION BY ADDING SINCE AND THE FIRST ACTION.

Example: *Why are you taking a math class?*
I am taking a math class *since I have trouble with fractions.*

1. Why did Mrs. Phillips fire Martha?

   Mrs. Phillips fired Martha _____

2. Why are you buying a tuxedo?

   I am buying a tuxedo _____

3. Why can your son skip the second grade?

   My son can skip the second grade _____

4. Why is the roof leaking?

   The roof is leaking _____

5. Why are you moving the furniture around?

   I am moving the furniture around _____

THE SENTENCE BELOW USES SO IN ANSWERING THIS WHY QUESTION.

Why did Mr. Ross tie up his dog?

The dog was chasing cars, **so** Mr. Ross tied up his dog.

DIRECTIONS: FINISH THE ANSWER TO EACH WHY QUESTION BY ADDING THE FIRST ACTION.

Example: *Why did Mr. Peterson fix the bike?*

The bike had a flat tire, _____ so Mr. Peterson fixed it.

1. Why did you give the dog a bath?

_____ so I gave him a bath.

2. Why did the man yell?

_____ so the man yelled.

3. Why will Mrs. Jetson go fishing?

_____ so Mrs. Jetson will go fishing.

4. Why is the teacher borrowing a dime?

_____ so the teacher is borrowing a dime.

5. Why did you call the police?

_____ so I called the police.

Example: Why are you crying?

_____*I am upset*_____ because I lost my wallet.

or: I lost my wallet, so _____*I am upset.*_____

1. Why are you going to a movie?

_____ because I am bored.

2. Why is Kathleen quitting school?

She is going to get married, so _____

3. Why did Mr. Rosen's son learn Spanish?

_____ since he is moving to the Southwest.

4. Why does the doctor want to see Mr. Simms?

_____ because she needs to change his medicine.

5. Why will your wife go back to work?

She wants money to buy a car, so _____

6. Why did Glenn mail his income tax forms early?

_____ since he needs his refund.

7. Why did the Elliotts move to Florida?

_____ because they both retired.

8. Why are they staying home tonight?

_____ since they are tired.

DIRECTIONS: ADD THE FIRST ACTION TO COMPLETE THE ANSWER TO EACH WHY QUESTION.

Example: *Why did Mr. Burke tell a lie?*

Mr. Burke told a lie because ___*he was afraid.*___

or: ___*He was afraid,*___ so Mr. Burke told a lie.

1. Why did Mr. Bowman bake a cake?

   Mr. Bowman baked a cake since _____

2. Why does Mrs. Lake want a new office?

   Mrs. Lake wants a new office because _____

3. Why did your wife visit her mother?

   _____ so my wife visited her mother.

4. Why is she asking the time?

   She is asking the time because _____

5. Why will Mr. Burns take the bus?

   _____ so Mr. Burns will take the bus.

6. Why can he drive a car?

   He can drive a car since _____

7. Why were the lights off?

   The lights were off because _____

8. Why will they borrow money?

   _____ so they can take a vacation.

Example: Why will Mrs. Oates borrow that book about repairs?

Mrs. Oates wants to fix a lamp so she will borrow that book about repairs.

or: Mrs. Oates wants to fix a lamp so *will borrow that book about repairs.*

1. Why did her cat climb the tree?

   _____ so her cat climbed the tree.

2. Why are Mr. and Mrs. Duval buying a new house?

   _____ since their old one is too small.

3. Why will they have a bowling team?

   They will have a bowling team because _____

4. Why is Ted leaving the Army?

   He was injured during his basic training, so _____

5. Why can't we find the road to the lake?

   We can't find the road to the lake since _____

6. Why does Mr. Stanley live in the country?

   _____ because he likes to ride horses.

7. Why is Ms. Morse taking bookkeeping?

   _____ so she is taking bookkeeping.

8. Why did the police chief retire?

   The police chief retired because _____

Example: Why did Sheila become angry?

Sheila became angry because her date did not show up.

1. Why did Mr. Hardy get upset?

_____

_____

2. Why are they moving to New Hampshire?

_____

_____

3. Why did she open your mail?

_____

_____

4. Why did that tree fall?

_____

_____

5. Why will Mrs. Levy go to the sewing class?

_____

_____

6. Why is her face red?

_____

_____

COMPLEX SENTENCES OFTEN MAKE WRITTEN LANGUAGE MORE INTERESTING. IT IS EASY TO MAKE A COMPLEX SENTENCE FROM TWO COMPLETE THOUGHTS. JOIN THE TWO THOUGHTS WITH **BECAUSE, SINCE, SO, IF, BEFORE, OR AFTER.**

Two complete thoughts:
Mr. Baker got mad at his boss. He quit his job.

Some complex sentences:
Mr. Baker got mad at his boss, **so** he quit his job.
Mr. Baker quit his job **because** he got mad at his boss.
Mr. Baker quit his job **after** he got mad at his boss.
Mr. Baker got mad at his boss **before** he quit his job.

DIRECTIONS: PUT A ✔ NEXT TO EACH GROUP OF COMPLEX SENTENCES.

Example: _____ *Matthew bought a pool table. He likes to play pool with his friends.*

___✔___ *The Claytons ate at a Chinese restaurant because they like Chinese food. Their friends like it so they took them.*

_____ 1. The Browns bought a sailboat after they retired. They also bought some rods and reels since they enjoy fishing.

_____ 2. Bob went to night school so he could learn bookkeeping. He did well because he studied hard.

_____ 3. My favorite summer dessert is chocolate ice cream. It is cool and refreshing on a hot day.

_____ 4. I will tell you a secret if you promise not to tell. I won't tell Kay since she can't keep a secret.

_____ 5. Benjamin Franklin was a famous American. He was a printer, writer, statesman, inventor, and many other things.

DIRECTIONS: JOIN EACH GROUP OF SENTENCES TO MAKE A COMPLEX SENTENCE. USE THE GIVEN CONJUNCTIONS IN YOUR SENTENCES.

Example: You are foolish. You believe in the Easter Bunny. (if)

You are foolish if you believe in the Easter Bunny.

1. My sister took a week off from work. She wanted to have a vacation. (because)

_____

_____

2. The bank made a mistake in my checking account. I went to see the manager. (so)

_____

_____

3. Laverne has been very busy. She moved into her new house. (since)

_____

_____

4. Darren was happy. His mother gave him a toy to play with. (after)

_____

_____

5. We opened a charge account there. We began our Christmas shopping. (before)

_____

_____

6. Ms. Stavros may leave work early today. She comes in early. (if)

_____

_____

Example: I had to walk my bike up the hill. The hill was very steep.

I had to walk my bike up the hill because the hill was very steep.

1. The washing machine is broken. I will have to take the clothes to the laundry.

_____

_____

2. Big cities have many problems. They have a lot of crime, smog, and people.

_____

_____

3. The children were hungry. I made lunch for them.

_____

_____

4. The U.S. wants to have good relations with Mexico. Mexico is its neighbor.

_____

_____

5. Many people went to the beach. They got off work Friday afternoon.

_____

_____

6. I will rent an apartment with you. You pay half the expenses.

_____

_____

Example: I like the Fourth of July. There is so much excitement.

I like the Fourth of July because there is so much excitement.

The Fourth of July is a very exciting holiday. Many fun things happen.

_____
_____
_____

Friends and relatives like to get together. They have a big picnic.

_____
_____
_____

There is a lot of food. Everyone brings a different dish.

_____
_____
_____

The people eat lunch. They play games and have contests.

_____
_____
_____

At night the children and adults are all excited. They get to see the colorful fireworks in the sky.

_____
_____
_____
_____

64

DIRECTIONS: WRITE ONE COMPLEX SENTENCE ABOUT EACH PICTURE.

Example:

The dog chased the cat, so the cat hid behind the garbage cans.

1._____

2._____

Example: _Joe is holding the flag so Ted can hit the ball into the hole._

WRITING SENTENCES WITH CONJUNCTIONS

DIRECTIONS: WRITE **1** NEXT TO EACH COMPOUND SENTENCE.
WRITE **2** NEXT TO EACH COMPLEX SENTENCE.
WRITE **3** NEXT TO EACH SENTENCE THAT IS NEITHER
A COMPOUND NOR A COMPLEX SENTENCE.

Example: ___3___ *Mrs. Morris never cuts or trims her hedges.*

___1___ *My mother often cans vegetables, and she also makes preserves.*

_____ 1. Mr. Okamoto will sell his taxi because he is retiring.

_____ 2. Silver and gold are minerals.

_____ 3. We will enter the boat race if we can.

_____ 4. Are you enjoying the play, or are you bored?

_____ 5. Mrs. Milton and her daughter went shopping for a lawnmower.

_____ 6. Mrs. Conway didn't have any baking soda, so she used baking powder.

_____ 7. I can't afford a new car since I just bought a new house.

_____ 8. Mr. Pounds must lose weight before he goes to the doctor.

_____ 9. I enjoy snow skiing but not water skiing.

_____ 10. Potatoes and carrots grow underground, but tomatoes and squash grow above ground.

_____ 11. Cars, buses, and trucks cause a lot of air pollution, but we can't live without them.

_____ 12. Abraham Lincoln was President during the Civil War, and he wrote the Emancipation Proclamation to free the slaves.

DIRECTIONS: **JOIN EACH GROUP OF SENTENCES WITH A** CONJUNCTION **TO MAKE A** COMPOUND **OR A** COMPLEX **SENTENCE.**

Example: *Ms. Fine likes to go camping. She doesn't like to fish.*

Ms. Fine likes to go camping, but she doesn't like to fish.

1. Mr. Carpenter sent his daughter to camp. She is a Girl Scout.

_____

_____

2. Karen's long hair was always getting in her way. She got it cut.

_____

_____

3. Mr. McCormick belongs to our church. He is a very religious person.

_____

_____

4. The Stills need a new washing machine. They can't afford one.

_____

_____

5. I need to rent a carpet shampooer. The carpet needs cleaning.

_____

_____

6. Do you remember that man's name? Have you forgotten it?

_____

_____

Example: _complex_ Mrs. Ellis typed the letter _since she wanted it to be neat._

_____ 1. Our canoe had a leak _____

_____ 2. Fishing is a very popular sport _____

_____ 3. The Galloways have three children _____

_____ 4. Will we have enough time to change clothes _____

_____ 5. Thunderstorms can be frightening to children _____

_____ 6. Mary Shelley wrote the first story about Frankenstein _____

_____ 7. Most fashion models are very thin _____

1. _____

_____

_____

_____

2. _____

_____

_____

_____

1. _____

_____

_____

_____

2. _____

_____

_____

_____

EXPRESSIONS

over and over
Means: to say or do something again and again

Grandpa tells Ginny the same stories over and over.

off and on   now and then
Mean: not regularly

Mr. Adams goes to church off and on.

back and forth
Means: backward and forward

The expectant fathers paced back and forth in the waiting room.

sooner or later
Means: sometime; at some unknown time in the future

Jack is a reckless driver. He will have an accident sooner or later.

ANSWER BOOK ⟩

The answers for this book begin on the following page. The pages can be removed and stapled together before the student begins to work in the workbook.

Answers to page 2

1. _or_

2. _but_

Answers to page 3

1. in the afternoon
2. cats <u>but</u> not dogs
3. Mr. <u>and</u> Mrs. Lin
4. at the bus stop
5. peanuts <u>and</u> popcorn
6. on the train
7. tired <u>but</u> hungry
8. Christmas <u>or</u> Hanukkah

_no_ 1. Virginia was one of the Thirteen Original Colonies.

yes 2. Will you wear your uniform <u>or</u> regular clothes?

_no_ 3. The longest day of the year is in June.

yes 4. North <u>and</u> South Korea went to war in 1948.

yes 5. We are friends <u>but</u> not neighbors.

Answers to page 4

1. Cottage cheese, lettuce, <u>and</u> sliced pears make a good salad.
2. I like ice skating <u>but</u> not roller skating.
3. Do you want ham, cheese, <u>or</u> tuna fish for lunch?
4. Ms. Stanford will go to Hawaii <u>or</u> California for her vacation.
5. My husband likes to shop for groceries <u>but</u> not for clothes.
6. The third <u>and</u> fourth grades will go to the zoo tomorrow.
7. Jessica wants to be an engineer <u>or</u> a lawyer.
8. Turn right at the corner of 16th Street <u>and</u> Pennsylvania Avenue.
9. Most fish swim downstream <u>but</u> not upstream.
10. Mr. <u>and</u> Mrs. Rickey will go to Florida on vacation.
11. Is morning, afternoon, <u>or</u> evening your favorite time of day?
12. We will re-cover the couch <u>but</u> not the chair.

Answers to page 5

1. George felt <u>happy</u> (but) also <u>tired</u>.
2. Do you want <u>a sports car</u> (or) <u>a family car?</u>
3. Rita baked <u>a cake, two pies,</u> (and) <u>some brownies.</u>
4. <u>Two</u> (or) <u>more people</u> can sit at this table.
5. My sister can visit us <u>Saturday</u> (but) <u>not Friday.</u>
6. <u>Ms. Winters</u> (and) <u>Mr. Benson</u> went to Las Vegas and Reno.
7. We can watch the <u>basketball game</u> (or) <u>the movie</u> on television tonight.
8. Mr. Schultz likes <u>tacos</u> (but) <u>not chili.</u>

Answers to page 6

Poisonous Plants

Many <u>plants</u>, <u>seeds</u>, (and) <u>flowers</u> are poisonous. Some plants in your <u>home</u> (and) <u>garden</u> are poisonous. Apples are a good example. The <u>seeds of an apple</u> are poisonous (but) not the <u>apple itself</u>. <u>Peach seeds</u> (and) <u>apricot seeds</u> are also poisonous. You should not eat <u>wild mushrooms</u> (or) <u>berries</u>. They may be poisonous. Some animals may eat <u>poisonous</u> (and) <u>nonpoisonous plants</u>. Certain plants are all right <u>for animals</u> (but) not <u>for people</u>.

Answers to page 8

1. Mrs. Frank cooked roast beef, potatoes, _and_ green beans.

2. The Kleins will go to the game _but_ not to the party.

3. Tom _and_ Jerry are a cat _and_ mouse team in cartoons.

4. Do you want a camera _or_ a toolkit for your birthday?

5. They will go to Japan _or_ to Africa this summer.

6. Sally _and_ Cathy like to swim _but_ not dive.

7. My son doesn't like peas, carrots, _and_ spinach.

8. Everyone will go to the party _but_ not together.

9. April, June, September, _and_ November have 30 days.

10. The bus stops at the corner _but_ not in the middle of the block.

Answers to page 9

Mr. McClellan likes to bake. He likes to bake bread, cakes, _and_ pies. He doesn't like to bake cookies _or_ brownies. He likes to surprise his wife _and_ children with a delicious pie _or_ cake. Sometimes Mr. McClellan bakes whole-wheat bread _or_ cornbread _but_ not white bread.

Mrs. Santini owns a clothing store. She sells dresses, pants, _and_ many other things. She sells clothes for women _but_ not for men. You can buy hats, dresses, sweaters, _and_ night gowns. You may pay with cash, write a check, _or_ use a credit card. Mrs. Santini will gift-wrap anything for you _but_ not deliver it.

Answers to page 10
Here are some examples.
Are your answers like these answers?

1. Many people like peanut butter and _jelly_ sandwiches.

2. Mr. Johns plays tennis but _not golf_.

3. I need an "A" or _a "B"_ to pass this course.

4. The bus stops at the library but _not the bank_.

5. Mrs. Todd, Mrs. Harmon, and _Mrs. Reed_ painted the fence.

6. Your sister or _brother_ must sign the form.

7. Did Mr. Sadler buy the brown suit or _the blue suit_?

8. Mrs. Davis studied Spanish but _not German_ in college.

9. We sat on the beach and _watched_ the sea gulls.

10. The Taylors will go to Florida but _not to Miami_.

11. Mr. Brinson and _Mr. Harrison_ fished for a week.

12. People eat bacon and _eggs_ for breakfast, lunch, or _dinner_.

Answers to page 11

Did you use these conjunctions in your answers?

1. New York, Chicago, *and* are important American cities.

2. Will you vote for Mr. Smith *or* in the next election?

3. My grandmother used to feed the cows *and* every morning.

4. Why do you like golf *but not* ?

5. Everyday Billy runs *and* at the playground.

6. Mr. Willowby *and* go bowling on Tuesday nights.

7. Do you want to read a magazine *or* ?

8. My friend gave me a party *and* for my birthday.

9. I packed my clothes *and* / *but not* .

10. Ms. O'Riley likes to play tennis *or* .

11. Mr. and Mrs. Rogers will ride the train *or* to Florida.

12. Sunshine *and* make trees *and* grow.

Answers to page 12

Did you use **and** in your answer?

1._____

_____

_____

_____

Did you use **or** in your answer?

2._____

_____

_____

_____

Answers to page 14

_2_ 1. Will you wear your new dress, or will you wear your blue pantsuit?

_1_ 2. Mr. Chou wrote a long letter to his brother in Miami.

_2_ 3. My daughter is a good student, and she plans to go to college.

_1_ 4. Mr. Thompson likes to sail and to fish.

_2_ 5. "Gone With the Wind" is a famous movie, but I have never seen it.

_2_ 6. I will go to visit my friend, or my friend will meet me at the club.

Answers to page 15

1. The President went to England, and ~~the President~~ *he* met the Queen.

2. Margaret likes basketball, but ~~Margaret~~ *she* doesn't like football.

3. Mr. Duchman is a good boss, and ~~Mr. Duchman~~ *he* is also handsome.

4. Mrs. Swanson bakes at least three pies, or ~~Mrs. Swanson~~ *she* doesn't bake at all.

5. Canada is our neighbor, and ~~Canada~~ *it* is a beautiful country.

6. Mr. and Mrs. Watts bought land, and ~~Mr. and Mrs. Watts~~ *they* will build a cabin.

7. The swimmers saw the lifeguard waving, but ~~the swimmers~~ *they* couldn't hear him.

8. The stop sign fell down, or ~~the stop sign~~ *it* was knocked down.

Answers to page 16

1. The man wore a grey suit, and _he_ wore a red and grey tie.

2. The train will leave at 6:05, and _it_ will arrive in New York at 10:00.

3. Mr. and Mrs. Stevens didn't go to class, but _they_ studied their lesson.

4. Mr. Swanson will go to Miami, or _he_ will go to New Orleans next week.

5. The girl made her bed, and _she_ hung up her clothes this morning.

6. The clouds will go away, or _they_ will bring rain.

7. The bird took a bath, and then _it_ sat on the fence.

8. Ms. Watson washed her hair, but _she_ couldn't roll it up.

9. The students saw the film, and _they_ talked about it in class.

10. The boy saw the snake, but _he_ didn't scream.

11. Elizabeth Taylor visited the college, and _she_ answered questions.

12. My watch fell on the sidewalk, but _it_ didn't break.

Answers to page 17

1. My boss bought a new picture for the office, (but) she hasn't hung it on the wall yet.

2. The Simpsons have three dogs, (but) they don't have any cats.

3. The Mackenzies have a farm, (and) they have seven horses.

4. Do you want the trunk in the basement, (or) do you want it in the attic?

5. My sister bought a house, (but) she doesn't have any furniture.

6. My husband applied for a job at the bank, (and) I applied for a job at the college.

7. Mr. Diego planted the vegetables, (and) Mrs. Diego planted the flowers.

8. Can you babysit tonight, (or) do you have other plans?

9. We will paint the kitchen, (and) then we will buy a new kitchen table.

10. The Post is a good newspaper, (or) do you prefer the Star?

11. Will the train stop in Alexandria, (or) will it go to Washington?

12. Virginia became a state in 1788, (but) West Virginia didn't become a state until after the Civil War.

Answers to page 18

1. Give me a raise, (or) I will quit!

2. Mr. and Mrs. Jones will fly to Europe, (but) they will return by ship.

3. Our children play at the playground, (but) they must be home before dark.

4. Ms. Harwood comes from Maine, (and) she loves lobster.

5. The Boswell's dog barks all night, (and) it keeps everyone awake.

6. Mrs. Mann is allergic to poison ivy, (but) she is not allergic to poison oak.

7. Would you like iced tea, (or) do you prefer a beer?

8. Go to the car, (and) wait for me.

9. Will you come to my house, (or) should I come to your house?

10. The airplane left on time, (but) it didn't arrive on time.

11. The Whites celebrated their anniversary yesterday, (but) I forgot to buy them a gift.

12. Does Jim like to go to the theatre, (or) does he prefer sports?

Answers to page 19

1. The children played ball outside, _and_ the adults played cards inside.

2. Mrs. Gravely wanted a blue coat, _but_ she got a red one instead.

3. We can cook dinner here, _or_ we can eat at the Pizza Parlor.

4. I wanted to arrive on time, _but_ I was an hour late.

5. Does your husband mow the lawn, _or_ does he pay Bobby to do it?

6. My friend went bike riding, _and_ I went with him.

7. My daughter is a majorette, _and_ my son is on the track team.

8. Mr. White tried to find his car keys, _but_ he couldn't find them.

9. Clean up your room, _or_ don't go to the basketball game tonight.

10. We saw "Shields and Yarnell" on TV, _and_ it was a very good show.

11. He is wrong, _but_ he won't admit it.

12. Don't tell my secret, _or_ I won't tell you another one.

Answers to page 20

_✓_ 1. Mr. Matthews took the Boy Scouts fishing, but his own son stayed home.

_____ 2. Herb found a dollar on the sidewalk, and Rita learned to use the calculator.

_✓_ 3. The children will go on a trip today, but their mother will stay at home.

_✓_ 4. The United States has a Congress, and Great Britian has a Parliament.

_____ 5. Do you like to visit your mother-in-law, or do you like to grow a mustache?

_✓_ 6. Africa is a large continent, and it is made up of many different countries.

Answers to page 21

_3_ Alaska is the largest state in the United States, ...

_7_ The first day of spring is in March, ...

_9_ The Petersons may drive to California, ...

_1_ The police department does a good job, ...

_2_ Would you like to go out tonight, ...

_6_ A large office building has many clerical workers, ...

_8_ Texas is a big and beautiful state, ...

_4_ Ms. Stanski found a wallet in the store, ...

_5_ The Marlowes will look for a new apartment, ...

Answers to page 22

1. _3_ the ice was too thin.

2. _1_ Several people saw the smoke,

3. _2_ and

4. _1_ The parade began at noon,

5. _2_ or

6. _3_ will he pay the bill?

7. _1_ Do you want coffee,

8. _2_ but

Answers to page 23

1. It is spring. The flowers are blooming. (and)
   It is spring, and the flowers are blooming.

2. Mr. Darwin made a bookshelf for his wife. His wife wanted a sewing table. (but)
   Mr. Darwin made a bookshelf for his wife, but his wife wanted a sewing table.

3. Some people like to live in the city. Some people like to live in the country. (and)
   Some people like to live in the city, and some people like to live in the country.

4. Will they have a picnic? Will they go to the amusement park? (or)
   Will they have a picnic, or will they go to the amusement park?

5. The children will stay with their grandmother for three weeks. My husband and I will stay home. (but)
   The children will stay with their grandmother for three weeks, but my husband and I will stay home.

6. Did the team win the tournament? Did they lose it? (or)
   Did the team win the tournament, or did they lose it?

Answers to page 24

Example:

My cat sleeps all day, but he prowls around at night.

1. *Please hurry, or we will be late.*
2. *My mother owns a dairy farm, and she raises prize-winning cows.*
3. *Mrs. Williamson drives the car to work, but her husband takes the bus.*
4. *Mr. Godfrey likes to cook, and his wife likes to work on cars.*
5. *Will you go to the store, or will you send your son?*

Answers to page 25

1. That painting is very good. You need a little more blue.

   That painting is very good, but you need a little more blue.

2. It is raining. We will go on a picnic anyway.

   It is raining, but we will go on a picnic anyway.

3. The new furniture arrived today. We sold the old furniture.

   The new furniture arrived today, and we sold the old furniture.

4. Ivey has a lot of work to do. Barbara has more.

   Ivey has a lot of work to do, but Barbara has more.

5. You better stop cheating. I won't play cards with you anymore.

   You better stop cheating, or I won't play cards with you anymore.

6. The Kaufmans followed the officer's directions. They soon found the college.

   The Kaufmans followed the officer's directions, and they soon found the college.

Answers to page 26

Our dog Bullet became sick. We had to take him to the vet. *Our dog Bullet became sick, and we had to take him to the vet.* We didn't want to. We had to. *We didn't want to, but we had to.* The doctor examined Bullet. He said our dog needed some medicine. *The doctor examined Bullet, and he said our dog needed some medicine.*

The dog could have pills. He could have a shot. *The dog could have pills, or he could have a shot.*

We chose the shot. The vet gave the dog one. *We choose the shot, and the vet gave the dog one.*

We went home. Bullet had to stay at the hospital. *We went home, but Bullet had to stay at the hospital.*

Answers to page 27
Did you use **and, or,** or **but** in your sentences?

1. My brother-in-law is an electrician, _____

   _____

2. We often have summer thunderstorms, _____

   _____

3. My cat and dog have flea collars, _____

   _____

4. Earthquakes cause a lot of damage, _____

   _____

5. Tomorrow I must pull the weeds from the garden, _____

   _____

6. Ms. Darrow will be a witness at a court trial, _____

   _____

7. January and February are the coldest months of the year, _____

   _____

8. The Averys sold their big house, _____

   _____

Answers to page 28
Show your answers to your teacher

1. _____ . . . _____ ,
   and ____ the men baked the cakes.

2. _____ . . . _____ ,
   or ____ do you want to go to jail?

3. _____ . . . _____ ,
   but ____ the man couldn't find his way home.

4. _____ . . . _____ ,
   but ____ Mrs. Farmer didn't see it.

5. _____ . . . _____ ,
   or ____ will he go fishing?

6. _____ . . . _____ ,
   but ____ I don't like prunes.

7. _____ . . . _____ ,
   and ____ then they went shopping.

8. _____ . . . _____ ,
   but ____ the judge wouldn't accept his answer.

Answers to page 29
Here are some examples.
Are your answers like these answers?

1. *Mrs. Nordwall is cutting the hedge, and Mr. Nordwall is mowing the lawn.*

2. *Mr. Peterson likes coffee, but he does not like tea.*

Answers to page 30
Do your sentences have **and, or,** or **but** in them?
Show your answers to your teacher.

Example: *The parents want their children to win, or they will be disappointed.*

_____

_____

_____

_____

_____

Answers to page 32

1. *since*

 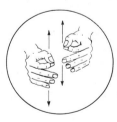

2. *so*   3. *if*

4. *before*   5. *after*

Answers to page 33

___✓___ 1. March is a windy month

___X___ 2. after they were married

___X___ 3. because the pond is very deep

___✓___ 4. we don't have much time

___X___ 5. since I found a $5.00 bill

___✓___ 6. the cat scratched the dog on the nose

Answers to page 34

_no_ 1. Franz went to visit relatives in Europe.

yes 2. I had been sick <u>before</u> I was caught in the rain.

yes 3. Please come by my house <u>if</u> you get a chance.

_no_ 4. Ms. Nunnally received an invitation to the banquet.

yes 5. Farmers must rise early <u>since</u> they have so much work to do.

_no_ 6. Will you spend the night in Richmond?

_no_ 7. Sesame Street is a popular children's TV show.

yes 8. Dinner will be served at 6:30 <u>after</u> the guests arrive.

_no_ 9. Many historical buildings are in good condition.

yes 10. The government requires warnings on cigarettes <u>because</u> smoking isn't good for your health.

Answers to page 35

1. <u>Paul was late for work</u> (because) he overslept.

2. <u>I will go with you</u> (if) you want me to.

3. <u>Mrs. Taylor will type that letter</u> (after) she eats lunch.

4. <u>His luck has changed</u> (since) he came to Washington.

5. <u>Your car may not start</u> (if) you forget to turn the lights off.

6. <u>Our company made a lot of money last year,</u> (so) I got a raise.

7. <u>Ms. Karas missed some of the movie</u> (because) she was late.

8. <u>Frances and Ken always eat dinner</u> (after) they watch the news.

9. <u>Sharon saved her money</u> (before) she took a vacation.

10. <u>A storm is coming,</u> (so) we cannot go sailing.

11. <u>Not many people want to live in Greenland</u> (since) it is so cold.

12. <u>Mr. Tomlin wanted to drink a cup of coffee</u> (before) he shaved.

Answers to page 36

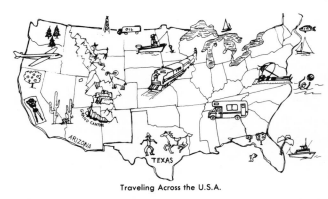

Traveling Across the U.S.A.

<u>Traveling around the United States can be fun if you like to travel.</u> You may want to go all the way to Alaska. <u>Alaska is a very wealthy state because it has so much oil.</u> However, you may not want to go that far. <u>You should go to the Rocky Mountains if you are interested in wildlife.</u> <u>Arizona is a good place to visit because the Grand Canyon is there.</u> <u>Plan to spend a lot of time in Texas since that state is so big!</u> Water skiers and sailors will love the Great Lakes. <u>Don't forget about the East and West Coasts if you like pretty beaches.</u>

Answers to page 37

___X___ 1. George Washington had false teeth after your son broke my vase.

_____ 2. Mr. Gonzales will talk to the boss if he has to work late again tonight.

___X___ 3. The bees were swarming around the picnic because they were afraid of fire.

_____ 4. My wife helped me prepare my income taxes, so I took her to dinner.

_____ 5. The Baltimore Orioles did not win the World Series since they did not play a very good game.

Answers to page 38

__4__ Venus and Mars are the planets closest to the Earth ...

__1__ Rinny is a very beautiful dog ...

__6__ Many people like Farrah Fawcett-Majors ...

__7__ We will get a trophy ...

__2__ I must finish school ...

__5__ They will move to Utah ...

__8__ Dieters like watermelon and canteloupe ...

__9__ William Shakespeare was a famous English writer ...

__3__ A lot of people like to go shopping in January ...

__10__ Mr. Koslo is president of the Lions Club ...

Answers to page 39

1. Jerry couldn't run in the race _because_ he had a broken leg.

2. Mrs. Gilmore will get a raise _since_ she does good work.

3. Mark will play basketball this year _if_ his grades improve.

4. They will not come to the barbeque _because_ they don't like to eat meat.

5. My cat likes to go outside _if_ it's not raining.

6. Nancy must mail the letter _before_ the post office closes.

7. Fred drove his car to work _so_ he could leave early.

8. Mrs. Jacobs was happy _~~because~~_ _since/after_ she got a new job.

9. Margaret won't come to class _since_ she has a visitor from out of town.

10. We want to do something special for the children _so_ we are taking them to the Puppet Theatre.

Answers to page 40
Show your answers to your teacher

1. Mr. LeGrand won a model car race _____
   _____

2. My nephew must learn better manners _____
   _____

3. Most high school students study U.S. history _____
   _____

4. The United States is a great country _____
   _____

5. Mr. Mann will go to the dance with Ms. Cummings _____
   _____

6. Your dog is very lazy _____
   _____

7. Mrs. Schwartz has done a lot of traveling _____
   _____

8. Our family was arguing about the TV _____
   _____

Answers to page 41

Show your answers to your teacher

1. _____

   _____ so I will pass the test.

2. _____

   _____ because the jury found him "not guilty."

3. _____

   _____ since they heard that the plane would be late.

4. _____

   _____ because their coats were alike.

5. _____

   _____ so their children could see Santa Claus.

6. _____

   _____ since the chair was broken.

7. _____

   _____ so the car would be warm.

8. _____

   _____ because we were hungry for fish.

Answers to page 42

___X___ 1. The electricity was off, so Mr. Martin couldn't watch TV.

___✓___ 2. Mrs. Steele went to the dentist, and she was there 2 hours.

___✓___ 3. Some of the people wanted to ski, but the others wanted to sit by the fireplace.

___X___ 4. Mrs. James took Carl to school after they went to the doctor.

___✓___ 5. The women sat on chairs, and the men sat on the floor.

___X___ 6. The plane couldn't land because the fog was too thick.

___X___ 7. Our football players can win the game if they try.

___✓___ 8. Will the class meet tonight, or has it been cancelled?

___X___ 9. Mr. Barber will stop at the store before he goes home.

___✓___ 10. The sun was shining, but it was a very cold day.

Answers to page 43

1. The Lions beat the Tigers (since) it was a better team.

2. The boy left camp early (because) he was homesick.

3. She doesn't want to drive downtown (since) the traffic is heavy.

4. I will help you with your work (since) I am not busy.

5. Ms. Hill doesn't want to learn bookkeeping (because) it is so difficult.

6. Mr. Lund can't go to the party (because) he has to work.

Answers to page 44

1. We bought a swimming pool for the children (so) they can enjoy the hot summer days more.

2. Mr. French worked 5 hours overtime this week (so) his family could have a little extra money.

3. They will have their cat spayed (so) she will not have more kittens.

4. Phyllis didn't have enough money for a bookcase, (so) she made one with boards and bricks.

5. Our apartment doesn't allow pets, (so) we will have to move.

Answers to page 45

1. The cheap brand of gasoline clogged my carburetor, **so** I changed brands.

2. We could smell the fresh bread **because** the wind was blowing toward us.

3. Ms. Corning paid to have the machine fixed **since** she broke it.

4. The moving company will take good care of your furniture, **so** don't worry.

5. You cannot pick up your sewing machine yet **because** you haven't paid the bill.

6. The train is too slow, **so** we will take an airplane.

7. We should cook the meat a little bit longer **since** it is still rare.

8. I have to buy the children some new clothes **since** school starts next week.

9. Mr. Stanley belongs to a chess club, **so** he has people to play chess with.

10. Marty doesn't want to go to the dance **because** he doesn't dance very well.

11. They didn't eat in the park **since** it began to rain at noon.

12. The dog couldn't jump the fence, **so** it crawled under the gate.

Answers to page 46

1. We were tired of waiting, **so** we went to the play without them.

2. I will be home tonight **so** you can come to visit me.

3. Ted wants a new blow dryer for his birthday **because** his old one broke last week.

4. Mr. Matthews took a long vacation **because** he did not have a vacation last year.

5. The children did not have to go to school today **since** it snowed four inches last night.

6. The Stallone sisters returned to New York **so** they could visit their family and friends.

7. Brenda has a good idea **because** it will save our club some money.

8. My mother is babysitting **so** my husband and I can celebrate our anniversary.

9. Mr. Bradford didn't write me a letter **since** he didn't know my address.

10. We put the birds in the bathroom **so** we could clean out their cage.

11. Smoke alarms are important **because** they warn people of fires.

12. The baby hasn't cried **since** I fed her.

Answers to page 47

1. The library didn't open until 9:00, so we had to wait outside for 10 minutes.

2. The little boy cried because he was afraid.

3. We don't go to the movies much since we bought a giant screen color TV.

4. Belinda's car had a dent, so she took it to have it fixed.

5. The union leader will talk to management since we did not get our pay increase.

6. The shelf in the kitchen needs to be replaced, so I will need to buy a piece of wood.

7. The soldiers went on leave because the sergeant dismissed them.

8. In January we went to Vermont since it is so beautiful there in the wintertime.

9. The mountain climber climbed all day, so he was very tired that night.

10. The police detective arrested the wrong person because he did not gather enough information about the crime.

Answers to page 48

yes 1. It was a beautiful day so we had the party outside.

_no_ 2. The Kinneys are moving next week ~~because~~ *so* they will need our help.

yes 3. It was their silver wedding anniversary, so we gave them a silver gravy boat.

_no_ 4. Colorado is a beautiful state ~~since~~ *so* we plan to go there on vacation.

_no_ 5. We were hot and perspiring ~~because~~ *since* we played tennis.

_no_ 6. It was the 4th of July ~~because~~ *so* Mr. Bright bought some fireworks.

yes 7. Allan wants to buy his wife some flowers since he wants to make her happy.

yes 8. The store was giving free tickets to the circus so we went shopping there.

_no_ 9. She was late to work ~~because~~ *since* she had to change a tire on her car.

yes 10. Most people like to sleep on Saturday because they don't have to go to work.

Answers to page 49

1. Mr. and Mrs. Chiang gave us two puppies *because/since* they had too many.

2. My sister and her husband will go to a party tonight *so* I will babysit for them.

3. Our church is planning a garage sale *so* we can earn money for a school.

4. The United States is a democracy *because/since* we have a "government by the people."

5. I like to go to the Astor Restaurant *because/since* it has good food.

6. Mrs. Clay will not have lunch today *so* she can lose some weight.

7. Ms. Gladstone wants to sit down *because/since* her legs hurt.

8. They plan to work hard Saturday morning *so* they can bowl Saturday afternoon.

9. Eat your vegetables *so* you will grow up to be strong and healthy.

10. I don't like to argue *because/since* it is a waste of time.

11. Mr. Taub has been feeling better *since* he had his surgery.

12. We decided to stay home *because/since* the streets were slippery.

Answers to page 50
Show your answers to your teacher

1. I will not have to water the garden _____

2. Mr. Lincoln cannot come to the meeting _____

3. Don't wash the dishes _____

4. Please come to my house _____

5. The children want to have a picnic _____

6. Thanksgiving is a nice time of the year _____

7. The Governor visted the college _____

8. Leon has a good job _____

Answers to page 51
Did you use **so** in your answers?

1. We do not have any milk , *so* . . . _____

2. Mark knows all about taxes , *so* . . . _____

3. The Howes left us their house key , *so* . . . _____

4. The post office is on strike , *so* . . . _____

5. It will be a cold winter , *so* . . . _____

6. We bought a used car , *so* . . . _____

7. Our son had a fever , *so* . . . _____

8. The vaccum cleaner is broken , *so* . . . _____

Answers to page 52

1. Ms. Parker is on a diet since she is overweight.
She is overweight, so Ms. Parker is on a diet.

2. I took my umbrella because it was raining.
It was raining, so I took my umbrella.

3. We went to New Orleans since my father-in-law was ill.
My father-in-law was ill, so we went to New Orleans.

4. Mr. Blankman wore his brown suit since his blue suit was dirty.
His blue suit was dirty, so Mr. Blankman wore his brown suit.

Answers to page 53

1. My sister loves horseback riding, so she bought a horse.
   My sister bought a horse because she loves horseback riding.
2. Mr. Roberts is a business expert, so the university asked him to give a lecture.
   The university asked Mr. Roberts to give a lecture because he is a business expert.
3. The ice was thin, so Mr. Barker couldn't ice skate.
   Mr. Barker couldn't ice skate because the ice was thin.
4. The tailor needed more room, so he moved to a new shop.
   The tailor moved to a new shop because he needed more room.

Answers to page 54
Did you use **because** in your answers?

1. Why do you want a salad for lunch?
   I want a salad for lunch *because* ...

2. Why will Mr. Sturgis work late tonight?
   Mr. Sturgis will work late tonight *because* ...

3. Why can't Aunt Ruth come to visit us?
   Aunt Ruth can't come to visit us *because* ...

4. Why did the Clarks go camping?
   The Clarks went camping *because* ...

5. Why are her parents moving to Arizona?
   Her parents are moving to Arizona *because* ...

Answers to page 55
Did you use **since** in your answers?

1. Why did Mrs. Phillips fire Martha?
   Mrs. Phillips fired Martha *since* ...

2. Why are you buying a tuxedo?
   I am buying a tuxedo *since* ...

3. Why can your son skip the second grade?
   My son can skip the second grade *since* ...

4. Why is the roof leaking?
   The roof is leaking *since* ...

5. Why are you moving the furniture around?
   I am moving the furniture around *since* ...

Answers to page 56
Show your answers to your teacher

1. Why did you give the dog a bath?
   _____ so I gave him a bath.

2. Why did the man yell?
   _____ so the man yelled.

3. Why will Mrs. Jetson go fishing?
   _____ so Mrs. Jetson will go fishing.

4. Why is the teacher borrowing a dime?
   _____ so the teacher is borrowing a dime.

5. Why did you call the police?
   _____ so I called the police.

Answers to page 57

Show your answers to your teacher

Answers to page 58

Show your answers to your teacher

Answers to page 59

Show your answers to your teacher

Answers to page 60

Show your answers to your teacher

Answers to page 61

✓ 1. The Browns bought a sailboat after they retired. They also bought some rods and reels since they enjoy fishing.

✓ 2. Bob went to night school so he could learn bookkeeping. He did well because he studied hard.

___ 3. My favorite summer dessert is chocolate ice cream. It is cool and refreshing on a hot day.

✓ 4. I will tell you a secret if you promise not to tell. I won't tell Kay since she can't keep a secret.

___ 5. Benjamin Franklin was a famous American. He was a printer, writer, statesman, inventor, and many other things.

Answers to page 62

1. My sister took a week off from work. She wanted to have a vacation. (because)

My sister took a week off work because she wanted to have a vacation.

2. The bank made a mistake in my checking account. I went to see the manager. (so)

The bank made a mistake in my checking account so I went to see the manager.

3. Laverne has been very busy. She moved into her new house. (since)

Laverne has been very busy since she moved into her new house.

4. Darren was happy. His mother gave him a toy to play with. (after)

Darren was happy after his mother gave him a toy to play with.

5. We opened a charge account there. We began our Christmas shopping. (before)

We opened a charge account there before we began our Christmas shopping.

6. Ms. Stavros may leave work early today. She comes in early. (if)

Ms. Stavros may leave work early today if she comes in early.

Answers to page 63

1. The washing machine is broken. I will have to take the clothes to the laundry.
The washing machine is broken so I will have to take the clothes to the laundry.

2. Big cities have many problems. They have a lot of crime, smog, and people.
Big cities have many problems because they have a lot of crime, smog, and people.

3. The children were hungry. I made lunch for them.
The children were hungry so I made lunch for them.

4. The U.S. wants to have good relations with Mexico. Mexico is its neighbor.
The U.S. wants to have good relations with Mexico because Mexico is its neighbor.

5. Many people went to the beach. They got off work Friday afternoon.
Many people went to the beach after they got off work Friday afternoon.

6. I will rent an apartment with you. You pay half the expenses.
I will rent an apartment with you if you pay half the expense.

Answers to page 64

The Fourth of July is a very exciting holiday. Many fun things happen.
The Fourth of July is a very exciting holiday since many fun things happen.

Friends and relatives like to get together. They have a big picnic.
Friends and relatives like to get together so they have a big picnic.

There is a lot of food. Everyone brings a different dish.
There is a lot of food because everyone brings a different dish.

The people eat lunch. They play games and have contests.
The people eat lunch before they play games and have contests.

At night the children and adults are all excited. They get to see the colorful fireworks in the sky.
At night the children and adults are all excited because they get to see the colorful fireworks in the sky.

Answers to page 65
Here are some examples.
Do your answers look like these?

1. *The family can't go on a picnic since it is raining.*

2. *The foreman is angry because the mechanic was late.*

Answers to page 66
Show your answers to your teacher

Example: *Joe is holding the flag so Ed can hit the ball into the hole.*

Answers to page 68

2   1. Mr. Okamoto will sell his taxi because he is retiring.

3   2. Silver and gold are minerals.

2   3. We will enter the boat race if we can.

1   4. Are you enjoying the play, or are you bored?

3   5. Mrs. Milton and her daughter went shopping for a lawnmower.

2   6. Mrs. Conway didn't have any baking soda, so she used baking powder.

2   7. I can't afford a new car since I just bought a new house.

2   8. Mr. Pounds must lose weight before he goes to the doctor.

3   9. I enjoy snow skiing but not water skiing.

1   10. Potatoes and carrots grow underground, but tomatoes and squash grow above ground.

1   11. Cars, buses, and trucks cause a lot of air pollution, but we can't live without them.

1   12. Abraham Lincoln was President during the Civil War, and he wrote the Emancipation Proclamation to free the slaves.

Answers to page 69

1. Mr. Carpenter sent his daughter to camp. She is a Girl Scout.

Mr. Carpenter sent his daughter to camp since she is a Girl Scout.

2. Karen's long hair was always getting in her way. She got it cut.

Karen's long hair was always getting in her way so before she got it cut.

3. Mr. McCormick belongs to our church. He is a very religious person.

Mr. McCormick belongs to our church, and he is a very religious person.

4. The Stills need a new washing machine. They can't afford one.

The Stills need a new washing machine, but they can't afford one.

5. I need to rent a carpet shampooer. The carpet needs cleaning.

I need to rent a carpet shampooer because the carpet needs cleaning.

6. Do you remember that man's name? Have you forgotten it?

Do you remember that man's name, or have you forgotten it?

Answers to page 70

Show your answers to your teacher

_____ 1. Our canoe had a leak _____

_____ 2. Fishing is a very popular sport _____

_____ 3. The Galloways have three children _____

_____ 4. Will we have enough time to change clothes _____

_____ 5. Thunderstorms can be frightening to children _____

_____ 6. Mary Shelley wrote the first story about Frankenstein _____

_____ 7. Most fashion models are very thin _____

Answers to page 71

Show your answers to your teacher

Answers to page 72

Show your answers to your teacher